Usborne Engli

Level 3

THE HOUND OF THE BASKERVILLES

Retold by Kamini Khanduri

Illustrated by Daniele Dickmann

English language consultant: Peter Viney

Contents

You can listen to the story online here:
www.usborneenglishreaders.com/
houndofthebaskervilles

"Good morning, Holmes," said Dr. Watson. He was just closing the door to 221B Baker Street when the famous detective said, "Wait, Watson. I'm expecting a visitor."

Another man came in. "Mr. Holmes, I'm glad to meet you," he said. "My name is Dr. Mortimer. I hope you can help me."

He took an old book from his pocket. "My friend, Sir Charles Baskerville, died suddenly three months ago," he said. "Before he died, he gave me this: the legend of Hugo Baskerville. Hugo lived 250 years ago. He was a terrible man. One night he kidnapped a farmer's daughter, took her back to Baskerville Hall and locked her in a bedroom. The poor girl climbed out of the window and escaped. When Hugo found out, he jumped on his horse and rode after her."

"What happened?" asked Holmes.

"Hugo's horse came back – without Hugo. His servants found the girl's dead body on the moor, with Hugo's body nearby. And there, in the moonlight, standing over him, was an enormous black hound."

"Now let me read you a newspaper story," Dr. Mortimer continued.

"Sir Charles Baskerville, of Baskerville Hall, has died. His body was found by his servant, Barrymore. Sir Charles used to walk in the Hall gardens every evening, but that evening he didn't return. Barrymore followed his master's footprints to a gate onto the moor. Sir Charles had obviously waited beside the gate. After that, his footprints were further apart. Finally Barrymore found his body. Dr. James Mortimer, a family friend, has said that Sir Charles had a weak heart."

"Is that all?" asked Holmes.

"No," said Mortimer. "Sir Charles really believed the old legend. Just before he died, I visited him. We were speaking at the door when he saw something behind me. He was terrified. I turned and saw a large black animal. Then it ran away."

"I see," said Holmes.

"There's something else," said Mortimer. "When Sir Charles died, Barrymore called me immediately. I saw Sir Charles's footprints, but there were some others beside them."

"A man's, or a woman's?" asked Holmes.

Mortimer whispered. "They were the footprints of a giant hound!"

"How interesting," said Holmes. "Do you believe this hound is real?"

"There are stories," said Mortimer. "Local people have seen a strange animal on the moor. It sounds like the hound in the legend. They say it glows with pale light."

"Who lives at Baskerville Hall now?" asked Holmes.

"Nobody," said Mortimer. "Sir Charles had two brothers, but they're both dead. One was Rodger Baskerville. He was not a good man. The other brother died in America, years ago. His son Henry is the new owner. I'm meeting him today."

"I'd like to meet him, too," said Holmes.

After Mortimer had left, Watson asked, "What do you think?"

"I have some questions," answered Holmes. "Why did Sir Charles wait by the gate? Why did his footprints change? I think he was running, Watson – running for his life!"

The next day, Mortimer brought a young man to Baker Street. "This is Sir Henry Baskerville."

"Well, Mr. Holmes," said Sir Henry. "Mortimer told me about your conversation, but I was planning to visit you anyway." He put a letter on the table. "This arrived at my hotel this morning."

The words were cut from a newspaper and stuck on the paper. They said:

If you want to live, stay away from the moor.

"Someone wanted to hide their writing," said Holmes. "Has anything else happened?"

"I've lost one of my new brown boots!" said Sir Henry. "I left them outside my room last night, and this morning, one was missing. The hotel can't explain it."

As soon as Sir Henry and Mortimer left, Holmes put on his coat. "Hurry, Watson!" he said. "We must follow them." Together they walked along the street after the two men. Suddenly Holmes pointed at a cab just behind them. Inside it was a man with a big, black beard. Then the man shouted, and the cab drove away.

"Who was that?" asked Watson.

"I don't know," said Holmes. "But someone left that letter at Sir Henry's hotel, and someone stole his boot. Maybe that was our man."

"I wish we knew the number of the cab," said Watson.

"We do," said Holmes. "It's 2704."

That afternoon, Holmes and Watson visited the hotel. Sir Henry had one dusty, black boot in his hand.

"Last night they took a brown boot," he said, "and today they've taken a black one!"

"Hmm, very strange," said Holmes. "Sir Henry, I think you should go to Baskerville Hall. I'm afraid I must stay in London, but Mortimer and Dr. Watson will travel with you. Watson will write with any news."

Later, another visitor arrived at Baker Street. It was the driver of cab 2704.

"I heard someone wants to speak to me," he said.

"Yes," said Holmes, "This morning, was there a man with a black beard in your cab?"

"Yes," said the driver. "He said he was a detective. He asked me to follow two men."

"Did he tell you his name?"

"It was Sherlock Holmes," said the driver.

Holmes laughed. "Watson," he said. "We are looking for a clever man indeed!"

Two days later, Watson, Mortimer and Sir Henry were on the train. It was a long, slow journey. At last they reached their station. A driver was waiting for them in a carriage. Outside the village the road became narrower, and there were almost no trees or houses. They were on the moor.

The carriage drove through some gates to Baskerville Hall. It was an old building, with high, dark windows. A tall man opened the front door. Watson noticed that he had a black beard.

"Welcome to Baskerville Hall," he said. "My name is Barrymore."

Watson and Sir Henry said goodbye to
Mortimer, who was going to his own house.
Then they stepped into a large room full of old
paintings. There were candles on the table and
around the walls.

They ate some
dinner, then went
upstairs to their rooms.
Although Watson was
tired, he couldn't sleep.
He could hear the wind
on the moor. Then he
heard another sound:
somewhere, a woman
was crying.

In the morning, he told Sir Henry. "Let's ask Barrymore about it," Sir Henry said.

Barrymore frowned. "There are only two women here," he said. "One is the maidservant. She sleeps on the far side of the house. The other is my wife, and it certainly wasn't her."

After breakfast, Watson noticed that Mrs. Barrymore's eyes were red. Was her husband telling a lie?

Watson decided to go for a walk. Soon he heard someone behind him. It was a small, thin man. He was carrying a metal box and a butterfly net.

"Dr. Watson?" said the man. "My name is Stapleton."

"I see that you are a collector," said Watson. "How do you know my name?"

"Our friend Mortimer told me. So, how does Sir Henry like his new home? We were all very sorry about Sir Charles. You know the legend about the hound, don't you? I think Sir Charles saw something on the night when he died. I believe he died of fear, poor man."

They came to a narrow path. "That's my home, Merripit House," said Stapleton. "I live with my sister. Come and meet her."

"Have you lived here for long?" Watson asked.

"For two years. I used to own a school, but there were problems and I had to close it. I had no more money. I am happy here, though. Look, do you see that wide, green part of the moor? That's Grimpen Marsh. The ground is wet and very soft. If you walk across it, you might never come back. Only I know a few safe paths."

At that moment, they heard a long moan which became a loud howl.

"What's that?" whispered Watson.

"The local people say it's the Hound of the Baskervilles," said Stapleton. "The moor certainly is a mysterious place." Then he shouted, "Excuse me!" and hurried after a butterfly.

While Watson was waiting, a woman appeared. Watson guessed that she was Stapleton's sister, although she didn't look like him.

"Go back!" she said. "Go back to London immediately!"

"But why?" asked Watson.

"I can't explain. Please, leave the moor! There is my brother. Don't tell him what I said."

"I see you've met Beryl," said Stapleton. He sounded less friendly.

"Yes," said his sister. "I was telling Sir Henry about our wild flowers."

"Miss Stapleton, you've made a mistake," said Watson. "I'm not Sir Henry."

"Oh!" she said. Her face went red. "I... please, forget what I said."

They walked together to Merripit House. The Stapletons invited Watson to stay for a meal, but he wanted to return to the Hall. He promised to bring Sir Henry to meet them.

Baskerville Hall, October 13th

My dear Holmes

I have so much to tell you. Two weeks ago a murderer escaped from prison nearby. His name is Selden. We were worried when we heard, but no one has seen him, so we hope he has gone from here.

Sir Henry shows great interest in Miss Stapleton. We visited Merripit House together, and since then we have seen the Stapletons almost every day. I think she likes him, too. Stapleton seems less happy about their friendship.

Last night, something woke me. I opened my bedroom door and saw a man. He was carrying a candle. I recognized Barrymore, and I followed him to an empty room. He stood at the window, holding the candle up and staring out across the moor. Then he blew out the candle and I returned to my room. What was he doing? I don't know, but this is certainly a place of secrets.

Your friend
Watson

Baskerville Hall, October 15th

My dear Holmes

I have more news. Last night, Sir Henry and I followed Barrymore to the empty room. Sir Henry walked in and asked, "What are you doing?"

Barrymore jumped away from the window. "Nothing, sir," he said.

I had an idea. "He's using the candle as a signal!" I held the candle up myself. A tiny yellow light appeared in the distance.

"Someone is answering the signal," I said. "Who is it?"

"I can't tell you," Barrymore answered. "It's not my secret."

"Then I will tell them." Mrs. Barrymore came into the room. "It's my brother. He's been out on the moor for two weeks, and we leave food for him. We use the light to tell him."

"So your brother is..."

"Selden, the criminal, sir. He came here on the night that he escaped. Please understand."

So the crying woman was Mrs. Barrymore. Of course she had to help her brother. However, when the Barrymores had gone, Sir Henry and I decided to find the murderer ourselves.

As we left the Hall, we heard the strange sound again. It came with the wind, quietly at first. Then it became a howl, wild and terrible.

We walked on towards the murderer's light. When we came closer, we saw a candle between two rocks. Suddenly a man appeared beside the rocks – a man with an evil face, a dirty beard and thick dark hair.

We leaped forward. The murderer turned and ran. We ran after him, but he was surprisingly fast. We were soon exhausted, and sat down on some rocks. At that moment, the moon came out from behind a cloud, and I saw the tall figure of a man on a rock above us. It wasn't Selden. Who could it be?

We miss you here.
Watson

The next morning, Watson finished his breakfast and thought hard. He didn't believe in ghosts – but what was the strange sound? If it was a real hound, why had nobody seen it during the day?

Sir Henry came in. "Barrymore has something to tell us," he said.

"It's about Sir Charles," said the servant. "I know why he was waiting at the gate that night. He was meeting a woman."

"A woman?" said Watson. "Who was she?"

"I don't know, but her initials were L L. Sir Charles had a letter that morning from the village of Coombe Tracey, in a woman's writing. After he died, my wife was cleaning his room and she found the letter."

"Most of it was burned, but she read the words:

Please destroy this, and be at the gate by ten o'clock – L L

A little later, Watson went for a walk. Mortimer drove past in his carriage, and offered to take Watson with him.

"Do you know a woman in Coombe Tracey with the initials L L?" Watson asked.

"That must be Laura Lyons," said Mortimer. "Her father, Mr. Frankland, lives nearby. Mrs. Lyons was married to an artist, but he left her."

"I should meet her," thought Watson.

A maid showed Watson into the sitting room. Mrs. Lyons was at her desk.

"I want to ask about Sir Charles Baskerville," said Watson. "You knew him, didn't you?"

"I did," she said. "When my husband left, I had no money. Sir Charles helped me."

"Did you meet him often?"

She looked angry, but answered, "Once or twice."

"Did you ask him to meet you on the day he died?"

"No," she whispered.

"You don't remember writing: *Please destroy this, and be at the gate by ten o'clock?*"

Her face went pale. "Yes, I wrote that!" she said. "I was desperate. My own father wouldn't help me. What could I do?"

"What happened when you went to the Hall?"

"I didn't go. It's true!"

"Why not?" asked Watson.

"Someone else helped me instead," she said. She refused to answer any more questions, and finally Watson left.

On his way back, Watson saw Mr. Frankland, who was standing outside his house.

"The police haven't caught the murderer yet," said Frankland. "I could tell them something. I know how he gets his food."

"Do you?"

"A child takes it to him. He goes by the same path every day. I watch him through my telescope. Come and see."

Watson followed Frankland inside and up to the roof. Through the telescope he saw a boy. He was carrying a bag and climbing a hill. At the top, he looked around, then disappeared.

Watson was excited. Selden's food came from the Barrymores, so perhaps the boy was taking food to the mysterious man? As soon as he left Frankland, Watson walked up the hill. When he reached the top, the sun was low in the sky. Below him was a circle of old stone houses. Watson walked down to the only house with a roof, and went inside.

No one was there, but there were blankets, plates and a bowl of water, with bread, cheese and fruit on a big flat stone. Suddenly Watson heard footsteps. He stayed very still. Then a shadow filled the doorway, and a well-known voice said, "It's a fine evening, my dear Watson. Come and sit outside."

"I thought you were in London?" said Watson. "I wanted everyone to think that," said Holmes. "I was staying here secretly, so that I could find out more."

Watson told him about Laura Lyons.

"Mrs. Lyons is very friendly with Stapleton," said Holmes. "If his wife knew, she wouldn't be pleased."

"His wife?" said Watson.

"Yes, that's another thing I've discovered. The woman you call Miss Stapleton is his wife, not his sister; although it's true that he used to have a school."

"Incredible!" said Watson. "That's why Stapleton doesn't like her friendship with Sir Henry." He thought for a minute. "So you mean that..?"

"I think Stapleton is our man. Now we must catch him, and I hope Laura Lyons will help us."

Suddenly they heard a scream. Both men jumped up. There was another scream, louder and closer. There was a new sound, too – a long, low moan, becoming a howl.

"The hound!" shouted Holmes. They started running. In the distance, they could see something on the ground. They ran faster, and found the body of a man lying face down.

"We're too late," said Holmes. "It's Sir Henry. The hound has chased him to his death."

They turned the body over. Holmes shouted excitedly: "A beard, Watson! It's not Sir Henry."

Watson recognized the face of Selden, the murderer. Barrymore had given him some of Sir Henry's old clothes.

"Remember, Sir Henry's boot was stolen from the hotel," Holmes said. "Stapleton probably gave it to the hound so that it could follow Sir Henry's scent. These clothes have his scent, too. That proves it, Watson – the hound is real!"

Sir Henry was glad to see Holmes at the Hall. During dinner, Holmes kept looking at the old family pictures on the wall.

"Who is the man in black?" Holmes asked.

"That's the wicked Hugo, from the legend," said Sir Henry.

After Sir Henry had gone upstairs, Holmes held a candle beside Hugo's face.

"Does he remind you of anyone?" he asked.

Watson looked. "Maybe Sir Henry, a little?" he said.

"Look again," said Holmes. He held one hand above the face.

Suddenly Watson saw. "He looks exactly like Stapleton!"

"I think Stapleton is a Baskerville," said Holmes, "the son of Rodger Baskerville. He plans to kill Sir Henry so that he can have Baskerville Hall and the Baskerville money. But we will stop him."

The next morning, Holmes told Sir Henry, "I'm afraid Watson and I must go to London. We can't come with you to Merripit House this evening. Please tell Stapleton. Take the carriage, but send it back and say you'll walk home."

"Across the moor?" said Sir Henry.

"Stay on the path and you'll be safe – but you mustn't leave the path."

Holmes and Watson went to see Laura Lyons. They explained that Stapleton's sister was actually his wife. Mrs. Lyons was shocked. After a few minutes, she said, "I'll tell you everything. Stapleton said he wanted to marry me. I trusted him completely. I never wanted to hurt Sir Charles – he had been very good to me."

"Did Stapleton tell you to write to Sir Charles?" asked Holmes.

"Yes, he told me to arrange a meeting that night. After I sent the letter, he told me not to go. He promised to give me the money himself. Then, when Sir Charles died, Stapleton said I would be in trouble if I told anyone."

"Mrs. Lyons," said Holmes, "you've had a lucky escape."

Holmes and Watson returned secretly that evening to Merripit House. Thick fog lay over the marsh. When they reached the house, they hid in the garden and looked through the windows. They could see Stapleton and Sir Henry, but Mrs. Stapleton wasn't there.

Suddenly they heard footsteps. Sir Henry was leaving. He passed the place where they were hiding.

"Is your gun ready?" whispered Holmes. Then he shouted, "Look out!"

They heard something through the fog. An animal was running towards them. Then they saw it: an enormous, black hound! Its eyes were burning red, and blue flames glowed around its body. It followed Sir Henry towards the moor.

Holmes and Watson pointed their guns and shot. The hound gave a terrible howl, but it didn't stop. Sir Henry looked back and screamed.

Holmes started running. The hound leaped on top of Sir Henry. Holmes shot again, five times. The animal finally stopped moving. The blue flames were still glowing.

"Look, it's been covered with a special chemical paint," said Holmes.

Sir Henry was shaking. "You saved my life," he said. "How can I thank you?"

Holmes and Watson ran to the house, but Stapleton had already gone.

Upstairs, they found a locked door. They broke it open, and found Beryl Stapleton. She was tied to a chair and she had a cloth over her mouth. They untied her and she asked, "Is Sir Henry safe?"

"Yes," said Holmes.

"And the hound?"

"It's dead."

Holmes wanted to look for Stapleton, but the fog was too thick.

The next day, Mrs. Stapleton showed them the safe path across the marsh. They followed her to an island in the middle, with a ruined house. They could see where Stapleton had kept the hound. It had been tied to a metal

ring. In one corner was a bottle of the chemical paint. Apart from that, the house was empty.

"That evil man surely fell into the marsh," said Holmes. "We'll never see him again."

Some weeks later, Holmes and Watson were sitting by the fire in Baker Street.

"That was a clever idea of Stapleton's! He used a real hound, but he painted it so that it looked like a ghost," said Dr. Watson.

"Yes," said Holmes. "Laura Lyons's letter brought Sir Charles to the moor gate that night. Stapleton was waiting nearby, and he sent the hound to frighten the poor man to death."

"And Sir Henry?" asked Watson.

"Stapleton started following him in London. Perhaps he meant to kill him there. He was wearing a false beard. He stole the boot to give it to the hound. The new brown boot didn't have Sir Henry's scent, so Stapleton stole the old black one."

"Who sent the letter to Sir Henry?"

"Beryl Stapleton. She was frightened of her husband. She cut the words from a newspaper so no one would recognize her writing."

"Poor Sir Henry! He has had a terrible shock."

"He certainly has; but he is alive, Watson, and he is young, and he will have a good life, I think. Now, shall we have some dinner?"

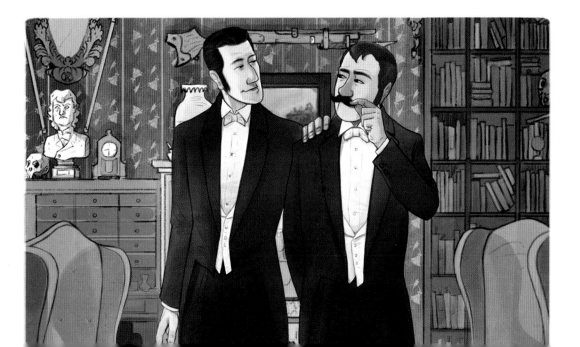

About Sir Arthur Conan Doyle

Arthur Doyle was born in Edinburgh in 1859. He studied medicine at Edinburgh University, where one of his teachers was Dr. Joseph Bell. Dr. Bell's intelligence and use of logic almost certainly inspired the character of Sherlock Holmes, many years later.

Dr. Conan Doyle, as he now called himself, began his working life as a family doctor in the south of England. He also began writing, first about his travels to the Arctic, then a story about a brilliant detective, *A Study in Scarlet*. The story appeared in a Christmas magazine in 1887. The characters of Holmes and Watson became more and more popular, and hundreds of thousands of readers bought *The Strand* magazine every month to follow their latest adventures.

Conan Doyle didn't love Sherlock Homes as much as his readers, and in the 1893 story, *The Final Problem*, Holmes seemed to fall to his death. Readers were delighted, then, to discover a new Holmes story in the magazine in 1901: *The Hound of the Baskervilles*.

Which two people?

Finish each sentence with names
of two people in the story.

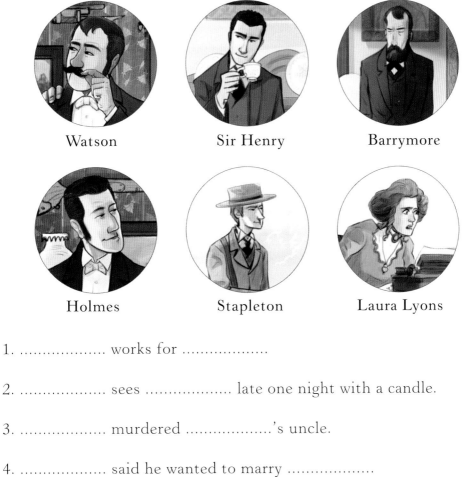

Watson   Sir Henry   Barrymore

Holmes   Stapleton   Laura Lyons

1. .... works for ....

2. .... sees .... late one night with a candle.

3. .... murdered ....'s uncle.

4. .... said he wanted to marry ....

5. .... says .... has had a lucky escape.

What happened when?

Can you put these pictures and sentences
in the order that they happened?

1.

"He looks exactly
like Stapleton!"

2.

"I was staying
here secretly."

3.

Sir Henry received
a letter.

4.

"I was desperate.
What could I do?"

5.

It was Selden,
the murderer!

6.

"You saved my life."

7.

Barrymore found
Sir Charles' body.

8.

"Miss Stapleton,
I'm not Sir Henry."

9.

"I watch him through
my telescope."

The Hound of the Baskervilles

Choose the right sentence for each picture.

1.

A. Hugo Baskerville was
   not a good man.

B. Hugo Baskerville was
   not a bad man.

2.

A. The dog ran away from
   Sir Henry towards the moor.

B. The dog followed Sir Henry
   towards the moor.

3.

A. The dog stopped moving, and
   the blue flames went out.

B. The dog stopped moving, but the
   blue flames were still glowing.

4.

A. The dog was there to frighten
   Sir Charles to death.

B. The dog was there to frighten
   Stapleton to death.

Mystery words

Choose words from the list to finish each sentence.

1.

"We're looking for a .... man indeed."

2.

"The moor is a .... place."

3.

Suddenly a man appeared – a man with an .... face.

4.

"We're too .... "

5.

Mrs. Lyons was ....

6.

In one corner was a bottle of the .... paint.

shocked	mysterious	precious	clever
safe	secret	late	evil
chemical	enormous	smooth	annoying

What do they want?

Match the speech bubbles with the characters.

A.

I want to help my brother.

B.

I want to know who stole my boot.

C.

I want to have the Baskerville money.

D.

I want to solve the mystery.

E.

I want to marry Stapleton.

F.

I want to warn Sir Henry.

Holmes

Beryl Stapleton

Sir Henry

Mrs. Barrymore

Laura Lyons

Stapleton

Word list

blanket (n) a thin bed cover made of wool.

butterfly (n) a flying insect with bright patterned wings.

cab (n) another word for a taxi, especially in the time when taxis were carriages pulled by horses.

candle (n) a wax stick that you burn to give light. Before people had electric light, they used candles.

carriage (n) something that you ride in, usually pulled by horses.

chemical (adj) made using a scientific process.

collector (n) someone who collects things, for example coins or stamps.

desk (n) a special table, used for work or study.

detective (n) a detective's job is to find things out, and particularly to find out about crimes and criminals.

doorway (n) the opening around a door.

flame (n) a fire is made of many flames.

footprint (n) the mark made by a foot.

footstep (n) the sound of someone walking.

friendship (n) when you are friends with somebody, you have a friendship.

glow (v) when something glows, it gives off a little light.

hall (n) a large and grand English house. A hall can also be the first room in a house.

hotel (n) a place where you pay money to stay the night.

hound (n) an old word for a dog, especially a hunting dog.

howl (n, v) when dogs howl, they make a long, sad noise.

initial (n) the first letter of a word, particularly of someone's name.

kidnap (v) to take somebody away from their home or family when they don't want to leave. Sometimes kidnappers demand money before they will bring a person back.

leap (v) to jump a long way.

lock (v) to close with a key, or to close a room with a key so that a person cannot get out.

maid, maidservant (n) a female servant.

marsh (n) an area of ground that is always soft and wet.

moor (n) a large area of open land, with rough grass and hardly any trees.

murderer (n) a criminal who has killed another person.

net (n) something made of thread, string or rope, with small holes. You can use nets to catch fish or insects.

scent (n) the smell of something, especially an animal or a plant.

signal (n) a way of sending a message using light or sound.

telescope (n) something that you use to see something a long way away. You might use a telescope to look at stars, or ships at sea.

Answers

Which two people?

1. Barrymore, Sir Henry
2. Watson, Barrymore
3. Stapleton, Sir Henry
4. Stapleton, Laura Lyons
5. Holmes, Laura Lyons

What happened when?

7, 3, 8, 4, 9,
2, 5, 1, 6

The Hound of the Baskervilles

1. A
2. B
3. B
4. A

Mystery words

1. clever
2. mysterious
3. evil
4. late
5. shocked
6. chemical

What do they want?

A. Mrs. Barrymore
B. Sir Henry
C. Stapleton
D. Holmes
E. Laura Lyons
F. Beryl Stapleton

You can find information about other
Usborne English Readers here:
www.usborneenglishreaders.com

Designed by Caroline Day
Series designer: Laura Nelson Norris
Edited by Mairi Mackinnon
With thanks to Andy Prentice
Digital imaging: Nick Wakeford

Page 40: Portrait of Sir Arthur Conan Doyle by William Henry Gates
(Private collection) © Bridgeman Images.

First published in 2018 by Usborne Publishing Ltd.,
Usborne House, 83-85 Saffron Hill, London EC1N 8RT, England.
www.usborne.com Copyright © 2018 Usborne Publishing Ltd.